MAGIC MATHS

Rose Griffiths

Illustrated by Julie Anderson

Hippo

Scholastic Children's Books,
Scholastic Publications Ltd,
7-9 Pratt Street, London NW1 OAE, UK

Scholastic Inc.,
555 Broadway, New York, 10012–3999, USA

Scholastic Canada Ltd,
123 Newkirk Road, Richmond Hill,
Ontario, Canada L4C 3G5

Ashton Scholastic Pty Ltd,
PO Box 579, Gosford, New South Wales,
Australia

Ashton Scholastic Ltd,
Private Bag 92801, Penrose, Auckland,
New Zealand

First published by Scholastic Publications Limited 1994
Text copyright © Rose Griffiths 1994
Illustrations copyright © Julie Anderson 1994

ISBN: 0 590 55326 7

Typeset by Rapid Reprographics
Printed and bound in Hong Kong

10 9 8 7 6 5 4 3 2 1

CONTENTS

HEY PRESTO 1

Do you want to try these magical tips for calculating quickly? It's unbelievable how fast you'll be able to work!

Show me what to do.

Let's start multiplying by ten and then by a hundred

Try these on a calculator, to see what happens.

1. 14x10
2. 10x7
3. 63x10
4. 10x92
5. 10x30
6. 236x10
7. 45x10
8. 10x27

A quick way of multiplying a whole number by ten is to write a nought at the end.

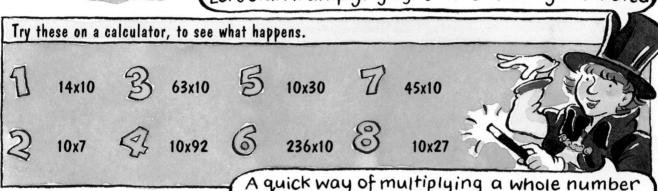

What do you think happens when you multiply by 100? Try these:

9. 8x100
10. 17x100
11. 100x62
12. 23x100
13. 31x100
14. 100x50
15. 100x85
16. 44x100

To multiply by 100, write <u>two</u> noughts at the end.

Now try some numbers of your own. Multiply by 10, or 100, or 1000! Check your answers with a calculator if you want to.

TRICK STICKS

Show your friends what a wizz you are by tricking them with these clever sticks. Use match sticks or lolly sticks (all the same length!)

WARNING DO NOT USE LIVE MATCHES!

Start with 4 sticks...

Start with 6 sticks...

Can you add 5 more sticks to make ten?

Can you add 5 more sticks to make one?

Can you make 10, with just 2 sticks?

The answers to these tricks are on Page 30. Can you make up some more puzzles like these?

I've got 24 sticks. Look, I can make 6 squares like this!

Can you make 7 squares with 24 sticks?

Can you make 10 squares with 24 sticks?

...or 7 squares with only 23 sticks?

Now use 24 sticks to make this pattern.

How many squares have you made?

Can you take away 6 sticks, and leave just 3 squares?

Think about big squares and little squares!

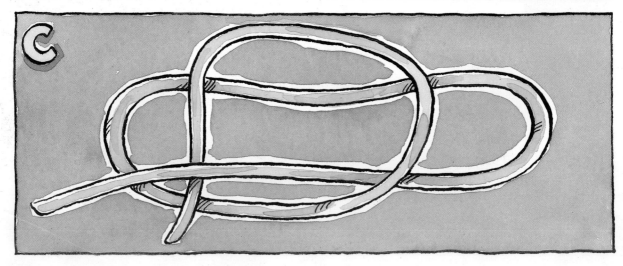

THESE RATHER KNOTTY PUZZLES ARE **TOPOLOGICAL** PUZZLES

Let me explain topology. This is a branch of maths which gets us to think about how places are linked together, and what happens when we bend things or stretch them.

Here's how to tie a special trick knot that we magicians sometimes use.

Gently pull your knot a bit tighter, then weave one end in and out, the way the arrows show:

It looks like a knot but it's not! Have a go yourself.

HEY PRESTO 2

I can multiply by 20 really fast in my head.

Show me how you do it then! Can you do this one? What's 20 × 16?

Ha! That's easy. First I work out 2 times 16.

Double 16... that's **32**

Then I multiply that by 10...

32 × 10... that's **320**!

(See page 5 for multiplying by 10)

Now, what's 20 × 12?

Um... double 12... that's 24... times 10... that's... **240**!

You can check your answer with a calculator if you want.

How could you multiply by 200?

How could you multiply by 30?

Try these:

1	20×14	**5**	20×20
2	20×34	**6**	13×20
3	20×17	**7**	20×26
4	20×19	**8**	15×20

HANDCUFF BLUFF

I tied a piece of string to each of my friend's wrists...

and I did the same, so that the two strings looped through each other.

But how are we going to get apart?

We're not allowed to take the string off our wrists and we mustn't untie or cut it.

This is a topological problem (like those on pages 8 and 9)

Here's how you do it:

1 Push a loop of your string under your friend's loop (the way the arrow shows).

2 Pull your loop over your friend's hand and then you will be free!

Phew! You had me worried for a minute!

VANISHING ANIMALS

Where have my friends gone?

I made them vanish!

Bring them back by joining up the points on my lists. You'll need some squared paper.

I'll practise by drawing something to eat!

and here's my list of points.

$(2,5) \rightarrow (2,1) \rightarrow (4,5) \rightarrow (2,5)$
colour this part in orange

$(3,5) \rightarrow (4,6) \rightarrow (2,6) \rightarrow (3,5)$
colour this part in green.

Here's my grid...

Here's how I started. (2,5) means the place which is 2 squares across, then 5 up.

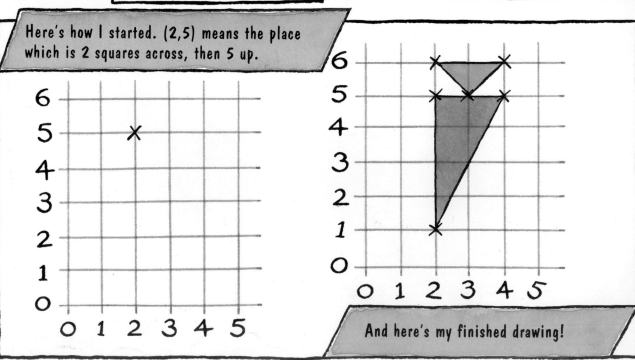

And here's my finished drawing!

14

Find out who my friend is!

First, draw the grid on squared paper.

Go carefully! Count squares <u>across</u> and then <u>up</u>. Join each point to the next one, as you go along.

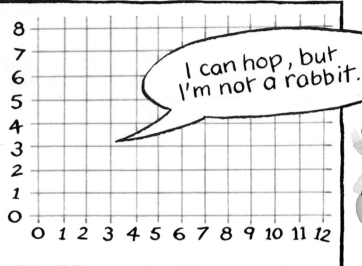

I can hop, but I'm not a rabbit.

Start with my back legs.

$(6,5) \rightarrow (5,6) \rightarrow (2,6) \rightarrow (1,7) \rightarrow (1,6) \rightarrow (2,5) \rightarrow (5,5) \rightarrow (6,4) \rightarrow (5,3) \rightarrow$
$(2,3) \rightarrow (1,2) \rightarrow (1,1) \rightarrow (2,2) \rightarrow (5,2) \rightarrow (6,3)$

Now do the rest of me.

$(6,5) \rightarrow (9,5) \rightarrow (9,6) \rightarrow (10,7) \rightarrow (12,7) \rightarrow (12,6\frac{1}{2}) \rightarrow (11,6) \rightarrow (10,6) \rightarrow$
$(10,5) \rightarrow (11,5) \rightarrow (12,4\frac{1}{2}) \rightarrow (12,3\frac{1}{2}) \rightarrow (11,3) \rightarrow (10,3) \rightarrow (10,2) \rightarrow (11,2)$
$\rightarrow (12,1\frac{1}{2}) \rightarrow (12,1) \rightarrow (10,1) \rightarrow (9,2) \rightarrow (9,3) \rightarrow (6,3).$

Draw an eye at $(11\frac{1}{2},3\frac{1}{2})$, and another at $(11\frac{1}{2},4\frac{1}{2})$

Three more of our friends are on pages 26 and 27.

15

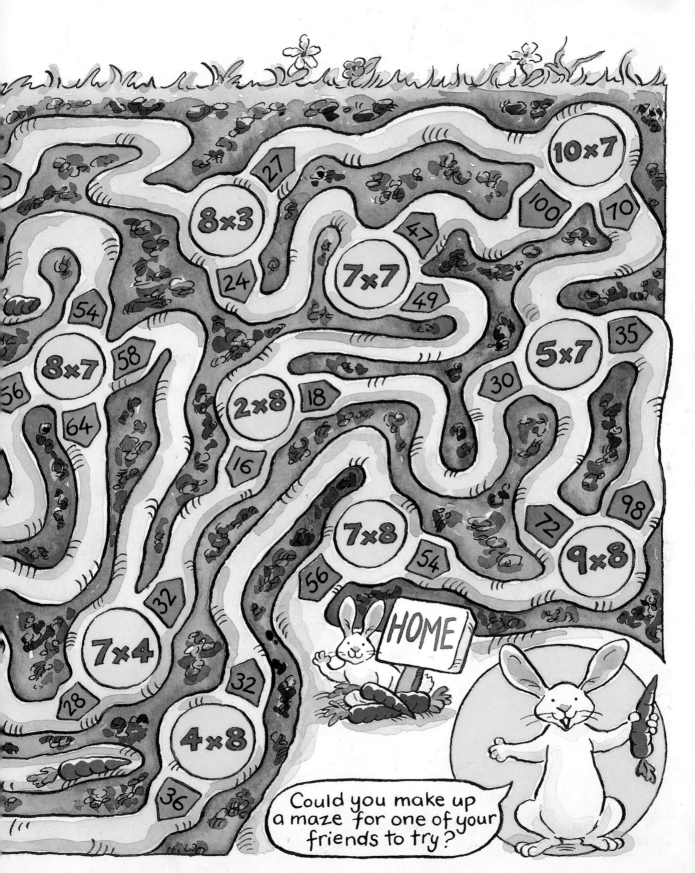

Now YOU try these:

1. 50x8
2. 14x50
3. 50x26
4. 22x50
5. 50x44
6. 50x15
7. 50x9
8. 7x50

I've got another mind reading puzzle. You can use a calculator if you want.

Doubling is the same as ✕ 2 = Find half of something by pressing ÷ 2 =

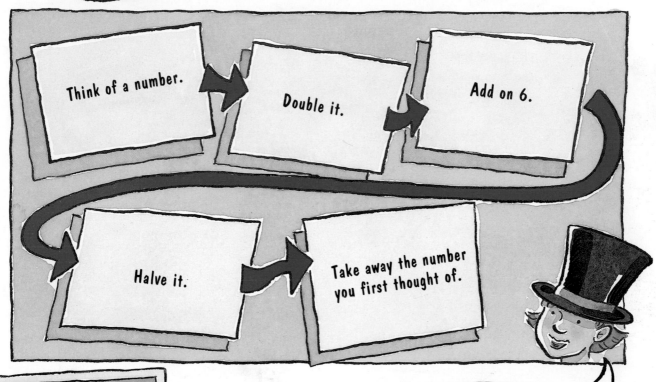

Think of a number.

Double it.

Add on 6.

Halve it.

Take away the number you first thought of.

I bet your answer is 3!

Try again, starting with a different number. Does it still make 3?

Do you know why these puzzles work? Could you make up one of your own?

23

Use tracing paper to finish the mirror picture on this page.

1 Trace the mirror lines and the bits of picture.

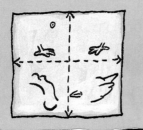

2 Fold your tracing paper along one of the dotted mirror lines. Trace over all the bits you can see.

3 Unfold the paper, and fold it up again a different way. Trace over all the bits you can see. Keep refolding and tracing, until you've drawn everything 4 times.

4 Open it out. What have you drawn?

Could you make a mirror picture with 4 carrots, please?

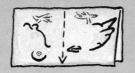

There is more Mirror Magic on page 29.

APPEARING ANIMALS

Three of our friends have vanished! Can you make them reappear?

Use the co-ordinates to help you draw them. Remember:- (1,4) means the place which is 1 square across, then 4 up.

1

I can swim, but I'm not a frog.

Join these points
(1,4) → (3,5) → (9,5) → (10,4) → (13,7) → (13,1) → (10,3½) → (3,3) → (1,4)
Draw an eye at (2½,4½)

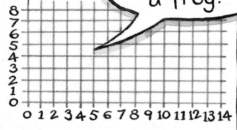

Now draw these: (4,5) → (6,7) → (7,5) and then (3½,3½) → (4,4) → (3½,4½)

(Look back to page 14 if you want to, for more help.)

Could you make up a co-ordinate picture?

Draw a different animal or object on a squared paper grid.

Write a list of co-ordinates. Give it to a friend to try it out. You could give them a clue if you like.

2

I like being in water, but I'm not a fish.

Start with my head.
$(8,8) \rightarrow (6,8) \rightarrow (5,7) \rightarrow (2,7) \rightarrow$
$(1,6) \rightarrow (1,4) \rightarrow (2,3) \rightarrow$
$(4,3) \rightarrow (5,4) \rightarrow (7,4)$

Draw an eye at (6,7), some nostrils at (1½,6), and draw my mouth from (1½,3½) to (2,4).

Now do the rest of me.
$(8,8) \rightarrow (10,9) \rightarrow (18,9) \rightarrow (20,8) \rightarrow (20,2) \rightarrow (19,1) \rightarrow (17,1) \rightarrow (18,2)$
$\rightarrow (18,4) \rightarrow (17,3) \rightarrow (10,3) \rightarrow (9,4) \rightarrow (9,2) \rightarrow (8,1) \rightarrow (6,1)$
$\rightarrow (7,2) \rightarrow (7,4)$

3

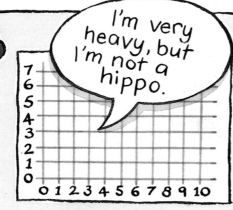

I'm very heavy, but I'm not a hippo.

Start with my body and legs.
$(5,5) \rightarrow (2,5) \rightarrow (1,4) \rightarrow (1,0) \rightarrow (3,0)$
$\rightarrow (3,2) \rightarrow (5,2) \rightarrow (5,0) \rightarrow (7,0) \rightarrow$
$(7,3)$

Now do my head.
$(7,5) \rightarrow (6,4) \rightarrow (5,5) \rightarrow (6,6) \rightarrow (8,6) \rightarrow (9,5) \rightarrow (9,2)$
$\rightarrow (8,1) \rightarrow (7,1) \rightarrow (8,2) \rightarrow (8,3) \rightarrow (7,3)$

Put my eye at (7½,4½)

HEY PRESTO 4

Who can tell me the quickest way of working out 99 × 8 ?

I know, I know... I'll show you my way!

Go on then !

99 lots of 8 is nearly 100 lots. 100 lots of 8 is 800...

and 99 lots will be 800-8, which is 792.

(See page 5 for multiplying by 100).

Right, now I'm going to try one.

99 × 12. 100 times 12 is 1200.

Take off 12... that's 1188.

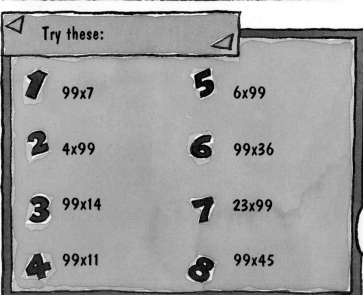

Try these:

1 99x7

2 4x99

3 99x14

4 99x11

5 6x99

6 99x36

7 23x99

8 99x45

Try some numbers of your own.

How could you multiply by 999?

29

ANSWERS AND HINTS

SUPERSTARS ☆
Page 4

When you use an odd number of dots to make your star, you can join up every dot without stopping. With an even number of dots, you can only "visit" half the dots in one go. Then you have to start joining again, from the next unused dot.

HEY PRESTO 1
Page 5

To multiply a whole number by 1000, write 3 noughts on.

TRICK STICKS
Page 6-7

TEN ONE

 ← This is X, the Roman numeral for ten!

(PS. In case you want to make up some more tricks using Roman numerals, here are their numbers from 1 to 10)

I II III IV V VI VII VIII IX X

You can make 7 squares with 24 sticks (lolly sticks or used matches) like this:

and with 23 sticks:

Here's 10 squares made with 24 sticks:

(8 small squares, and 2 bigger ones)

There are 14 squares here: (9 small ones, 4 middle-sized, and 1 large one).

With 6 less sticks, just 3 squares!

KNOTS OR NOT?

Pages 8-9

 A   Yes, it makes a knot

 B   Yes

 C   No

NUMBER JUGGLING

Pages 10-11

You can make six different numbers: 347, 374, 437, 473, 734 and 743. When you pick three number cards, the biggest turned back-to-front will always give you the smallest.

HEY PRESTO 2

Page 12

To multiply a whole number by 200, you could double it and write on two noughts. Or perhaps you've thought of another way!

VANISHING ANIMALS

Pages 14-15

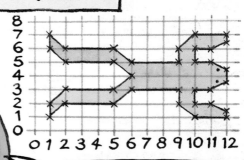

Did you find my friend, frog?

ESCAPOLOGY

Pages 18-19

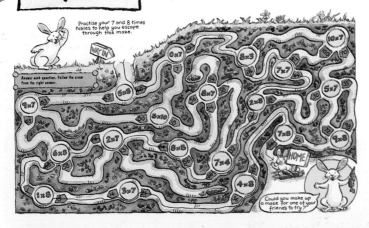

HEY PRESTO 3

Page 21

You could multiply by 5, then by 10, to multiply by 50. To multiply by 25, you can times by 100, then halve it and halve it again. Or you might have thought of <u>another</u> way!

I CAN READ YOUR MIND

Pages 22-23

A simple way of making up a puzzle of your own is to follow the same pattern as the ones shown, but change the number you tell your friend to add on. Try your puzzle out a few times first to check that it works, whatever number your friend thinks of!

MIRROR MAGIC

Pages 24-25

APPEARING ANIMALS

Pages 26-27

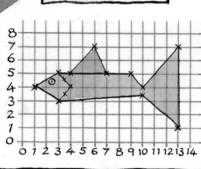
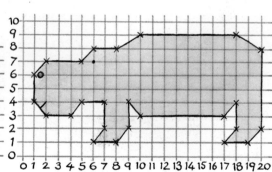
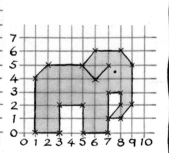

HEY PRESTO 4

Page 28

999 is nearly 1000...so multiply by 1000, then take away one lot.

MORE MAGIC MIRRORS

Page 29